FREE EXP

101 Fee-Free Contests, Competitions, and Other Opportunities for Resourceful Writers

Printed in the United States of America.

Booklocker.com, Inc.
2004

FREE EXPRESSION

101 Fee-Free Contests, Competitions, and Other Opportunities for Resourceful Writers

Erika Dreifus
Ed.M., M.F.A., Ph.D.

With heartfelt thanks

for my family, friends, teachers, colleagues, and students.

I'm lucky that so many of you have multiple identities.

Jan. 2004

And for Brett – this copy°

Thanks so much for your friendship. I look forward to receiving one of your books very soon!

All the best,

Erika

TABLE OF CONTENTS

INTRODUCTION

"What do you all think about contests?" one of my colleagues asked our online writing group. "Do you think you get a better read when you actually pay a reading/entry fee?"

No one responded to that query (publicly, at any rate).

Although I've entered many literary competitions, my colleague's question is not one I can answer, either. I've never administered or judged a contest, and frankly, there are just too many competitions out there for anyone to issue any generalizations about their inner workings. There are, however, some wonderfully useful articles in print and on the web that offer a variety of individual ideas about what prospective entrants might consider in evaluating potential competitions and preparing to submit work. You'll find some of these listed within the references included near the end of this book.

What I can tell you is that I've discovered many benefits that came with participation in writing competitions even when my work didn't "win." I've found some truly remarkable writing in the journal subscriptions that have accompanied some of those fees, for instance. In one case I was asked to participate in a public reading of my story—that possibility hadn't even been publicized in the contest guidelines. In other situations contest submissions have led to correspondence with other writers, and other assignments from editors.

But I think that my colleague's question about the reading fees itself unwittingly overlooks a crucial point: many contests that lead to publication—and similar opportunities for writers such as grants, fellowships, residencies, and retreats—don't require "reading" or "entry" or "processing" fees at all. Some writers believe they shouldn't have to pay such fees. Some just can't afford them. And still others perhaps simply prefer knowing that the "fee-free" option exists.

The first literary contest I won—a short story competition—was one of these fee-free competitions. (In fact, the year I won it was the second year I'd entered it—the fee-free contest can easily become a habit!) The success encouraged me to seek out additional opportunities, and to let others know about them as well. Soon I was finding so much information about prizes and grants and fellowships—and telling so many people about them—that it just seemed to make sense to compile everything in one place. It wasn't very long before I found I had so much material there was enough, literally, for a book.

So what will you find in *Free Expression*? You'll find contests and competitions—that don't charge reading, entry, or other administrative fees—that lead to publication of novels, short story collections, poetry collections, books of nonfiction ("creative" and "scholarly"), and children's literature. You'll find grants to help facilitate development of new work, completion of work-in-progress, and other professional opportunities. You'll find fellowships that will offer you time and space in artistic communities, at residencies and retreats, conferences and colonies. You'll find opportunities for student writers, undergraduate and graduate. And you'll even find a few places to turn in cases of emergency.

But if you still haven't found enough, that final reference chapter of *Free Expression* points you to additional sources for information on opportunities for writers that I hope will prove helpful in the future. In the appendices there's even space to jot down a few thoughts, plans, and projects you might wish to pursue right away.

Some things you won't find in these pages. For instance, you won't find competitions that require you to be a fee-paying member of an organization before allowing you to participate. You won't find awards offered by journals and reviews—for the best poem or story the journal has published in a given year. In fact, you won't, in general, find competitions or award programs intended specifically to recognize previously published work. Supporting new work (and quite often, new writers) is the main point here, which is why research and other opportunity grants feature so prominently, too.

Virtually every competition offers a cash award. Many also offer publication. Two exceptions I could not resist including—the Faux Faulkner and Imitation Hemingway contests, which feature impressive travel packages and publication in an international magazine, United Airlines's *Hemispheres*, for their winners. Authorial license here!

In the end, you may still choose to check out the costlier competitions. But at least now you'll have some choices as you seek to express yourself—in print.

Good luck with your writing, and of course, with your Free Expression!

    Best,
    Erika Dreifus
    Ed.M., M.F.A., Ph.D.

*Please note that **Free Expression** contains information collected from many sources, with the purpose of providing general references. The author has prepared the manuscript with utmost diligence to render it as accurate as possible, but readers are advised to verify information when necessary and appropriate. Please do not interpret any listing as an endorsement or recommendation.*

CHAPTER ONE
Getting Started: Ten Tips

1) Always learn about the sponsoring organization and, if an award program includes publication, familiarize yourself with that publication before submitting any contest entry. Just as you must research potential publishers for your short stories, essays, or books in other situations, you'll want to understand—and perhaps even better "match" your submissions—to a given opportunity. And at the same time, especially with programs and publications that may be new or unfamiliar to you, it's important to assure yourself that these are, indeed, places where you'll be happy to see your work find a home and recognition.

2) Check with the sponsoring organization's website (or by mail or phone if necessary) to learn about any changes in a program's guidelines or policies. Deadlines in particular may shift from year to year, even just to accommodate a weekend or holiday.

3) If you are requesting additional information or guidelines by mail, be sure to enclose a self-addressed, stamped envelope (SASE) with proper postage.

4) Plot the deadlines in your calendar (or use the space provided in Appendix A of this book). Plan ahead. Some writers use contest deadlines to spur them on to finish a project—or start a new one. Some set goals (one

competition per month, one competition per quarter, etc.). But if there's an opportunity that's just perfect for you, don't miss it because you "forgot" to note it when it first caught your eye.

5) You will also need to double-check every opportunity you're interested in pursuing for required entry forms and specific instructions on manuscript preparation and mailing.

6) Speaking of manuscript preparation and mailing—always follow the individual guidelines. Don't assume that all contest policies are created equal! And don't antagonize or irritate a contest administrator (or judge) before s/he has even read your work. Do not e-mail submissions to competitions that do not accept e-mail submissions. Do not send a manuscript with your name on every page if the guidelines explicitly state that your name should appear nowhere on the manuscript. Do not staple manuscripts that should be paper-clipped or bound. And so on.

7) Proofread, proofread, proofread. Then proofread again. Read your work aloud to catch the errors spellcheck or other computer programs may not have noticed.

8) Keep a record—and a copy—of all your submissions.

9) If and when you find yourself in the happy position of having your work win a competition, it is the kind (and polite) thing to do to notify any other publication or publisher who may be considering that work that it is no longer available (most organizations will indicate in their guidelines whether such a simultaneous submission was acceptable in the first place). Take care of any such notifications immediately.

10) Celebrate! (Whether you've "won" or not!) You've accomplished something pretty important just by putting your work out there and taking this chance. Give yourself some credit. And then get back to work!

CHAPTER TWO
Fiction

Here you'll find programs that award cash prizes and/or publication (or, in the cases of the Faux Faulkner and Imitation Hemingway contests, travel awards plus publication in *Hemispheres* magazine, the United Airlines inflight magazine) for short stories, novel excerpts, story collections, novel manuscripts, and/or works-in-progress. Be sure to check later sections of *Free Expression*, especially those covering Multiple/ Alternating Genres, Residencies and Retreats, and Student Opportunities for additional prize possibilities in fiction.

1
Warren Adler Fiction Award
Wyoming Arts Council
2320 Capitol Avenue
Cheyenne, WY 82002
Tel. 307.777.7742
Mike Shay, Contest Coordinator
mshay@state.wy.us
http://wyoarts.state.wy.us
Deadline: January 30 (postmarked)

Prize recognizes the best short story written by a writer living in Wyoming. Manuscript may not exceed 20 pages. An entry form, available on the website, is required. Previously published work may be submitted, but must be retyped and not submitted in reprint form. The author of the winning manuscript receives $1,000.

2
Nelson Algren Awards
Chicago Tribune Literary Prizes
435 N. Michigan Avenue, LL 2
Chicago, IL 60611
Submissions: November-February (send SASE for current guidelines)

These awards ($5,000 for the winner and $1,500 each to three runners-up; stories are also published in the *Chicago Tribune* and posted on the newspaper's internal site) recognize unpublished short fiction by American writers. Manuscripts, which will not be returned, must run between 2,500 and 10,000 words. Writers may submit up to two manuscripts; name should not appear on the manuscript but writers should include a cover sheet with name, address, phone number and entry title.

3
David Dornstein Memorial Creative Writing Contest for Young Adult Writers
Coalition for the Advancement of Jewish Education
261 W. 35th Street, Fl. 12A
New York, NY 10001
Tel. 212.268.4210
cajeny@caje.org
http://www.caje.org
Deadline: December 31

Open to writers between the ages of 18 and 35, this contest welcomes unpublished short stories of up to 5,000 words on "a Jewish theme or topic." It honors David Dornstein, who was a CAJE Conference Assistant killed in the December 1988 Pan Am plane that crashed in Lockerbie, Scotland. Awards include cash prizes and publication in *Jewish Education News*. If three winning stories are selected, prize money is divided $700/$200/$100; if two stories win, money is divided $750/$250. No identifying information beyond the story title should appear on the manuscript, but a cover sheet with the author's name, address, phone number and story title is required. Entrants must also include a copy of a driver's license or other document to prove age, and a signed statement attesting that the story has never been published.

4
Faux Faulkner Contest
Yoknapatawpha Press
PO Box 248
Oxford, MS 38655
Tel. and Fax 662.234.0909
faulkner@watervalley.net
http://www.hemispheresmagazine.com/contests/enter.htm
Deadline: March 1 (received)

Up to 500 words of fiction best capturing "the sound and the fury of Faulkner" will net a writer a prize of two tickets on United Airlines to Memphis, TN for a Faulkner conference—to read the winning entry. Prize also includes rental car, five nights' lodging at the University of Mississippi Alumni House, and publication in the July issue of *Hemispheres* magazine.

5
S. Mariella Gable Prize For Fiction
Editorial Department
Graywolf Press
2402 University Avenue
Suite 203
Saint Paul, MN 55514
Tel. 651.641.0077
wolves@graywolfpress.org
http://www.graywolfpress.org
Manuscripts considered on a rolling basis throughout the year.

Award includes a $15,000 advance and hardcover publication for one novel per year. Writers should submit a query according to Graywolf's guidelines before sending full manuscript.

6
Leslie Garrett Fiction Contest
Awards
Knoxville Writers' Guild
P.O. Box 10326
Knoxville, TN 37939
Tel. 865.428.0389 (Don Williams)
http://www.knoxvillewritersguild.org/leslie.htm
Deadline: January 31

Open to Tennessee residents over the age of 18, this fiction contest honors the memory of prize-winning novelist Leslie Garrett. Submissions may be unpublished short stories or novel excerpts, not to exceed 6,000 words. No more than two entries per contestant. A cover sheet should include the name of the contest, the writer's name, address, phone number, and e-mail address (optional). No identifying information should appear on the manuscript itself. Manuscripts will not be returned. Awards include cash prizes of $250, $150, and $100.

7
Grub Street Revision Fellowship

grub street, inc.
561 Windsor Street
Somerville, MA 02143
Attn: Jessica Bernard
Tel. 617.623.8100
info@grubstreet.org
http://www.grubstreet.org/programs/fellowship.html
Deadline: February 1 (postmarked)

This award is open to local emerging writers who have a completed draft of a novel, novella, or short story collection and who have not previously published a full-length book. "'Local' is defined as anyone who can get themselves to our Somerville offices twice per month," as the fellowship, which includes a $2,500 cash stipend, an in-depth review of the manuscript by an established writer, and a review of the finished manuscript at the fellowship's end by "a prominent agent and/or editor," also requires the winner to give a reading and hold office hours twice each month in Somerville. Applicants should submit the first 50 pages of the manuscript (with name appearing only on detachable cover sheet), project synopsis, a short description of revision plans, and resume. Complete manuscripts will be requested from finalists.

8
Imitation Hemingway Competition
Hemispheres
1301 Carolina Street
Greensboro, NC 27401
Fax 336.378.8265
hemiedit@aol.com
http://www.hemispheresmagazine.com/contests/enter.ht
m
Deadline: March 1 (received)

The author of the 500-word entry that shows the "best, clean, well-lighted Hemingway parody" receives two tickets to Italy on United Airlines, courtesy of *Hemispheres*, and has his/her entry published in the July issue of *Hemispheres*.

9
Iowa Short Fiction Award/John Simmons Short Fiction Award
Iowa Writers Workshop
102 Dey House
Iowa City, IA 52242-1000
http://www.uiowa.edu/uiowapress/prize-
rules.htm#SHORTFICTION
Submissions: August 1-September 30

Open to "any writer who has not previously published a volume of prose fiction." Novels are not considered; submissions of short story collections must number at least 150 word-processed, double-spaced pages. There is no application form. Winning manuscripts are published by the University of Iowa Press, under standard contract.

10
Minnesota Monthly Tamarack Award
600 U.S. Trust Building
730 Second Avenue S
Minneapolis, MN 55402
Tel. 612.371.5800
editor@minnesotamonthly.com
http://www.minnesotamonthly.com
Deadline: May (specific deadline available on website in January)

Open to residents of Minnesota, North Dakota, South Dakota, Iowa, Wisconsin and Michigan, the Tamarack Award competition offers cash prize and publication in *Minnesota Monthly* magazine. Short fiction submissions (no novel excerpts) must run between 1,000-3,000 words. See website for specific manuscript preparation guidelines.

11
North Carolina State Short Story Contest
Department of English
Campus Box 8105
NC State University
Raleigh, NC 27695-8105
wwbarnha@unity.ncsu.edu
http://english.chass.ncsu.edu/creativewriting/storycontest.htm
Deadline: early November (check for specific deadline closer to the date)

This contest, for short stories (up to 5,000 words or 20 double-spaced pages) and short short stories (up to

1,200 words or 5 double-spaced pages) is open to all North Carolina residents except employees of the UNC system and writers who have already published a book. In 2003 prizes included $500 for a short story and $200 for a short short story (final guest judge was Margot Livesey). Note: According to Professor William Barnhardt a generous grant will allow the contest to add prizes and honorable mentions in 2004.

12
South Carolina Fiction Project
South Carolina Arts Commission
1800 Gervais Street
Columbia, SC 29201
Tel. 803.734.8696
http://www.state.sc.us/arts
Deadline: January 15 (postmarked)

Recognizes up to 12 short story writers with publication in the *Post and Courier* and $500. Applicants must be legal residents of South Carolina, 18 years of age or older at time of application. See website for additional guidelines and required application form.

13
Thoroughbred Times Biennial Fiction Contest
P.O. Box 8237
Lexington, KY 40533-8237
Tel. 859.260.9800
http://www.thoroughbredtimes.com/
Deadline: December 31 (received)

"Designed to encourage and recognize outstanding fiction written about the Thoroughbred industry." Submissions may not exceed 5000 words and may not have been previously published or submitted to a previous *Thoroughbred Times* Fiction Contest. Winning entries receive cash awards (1st place, $800; 2nd place, $400; 3rd place $250) and publication in *Thoroughbred Times*. "Any Honorable Mention winners that are published will receive $150." See guidelines for additional information. NB: This is a biennial contest, with the most recent deadline December 31, 2003.

CHAPTER THREE
Poetry

While it isn't difficult to locate poetry contests, it's somewhat more challenging to find competitions that don't charge fees, aren't recognizing work previously published (as in "best of" or "editor's choice" among all the issues of a given journal for a given year), or don't require membership in the sponsoring organization before waiving an entry fee. (This isn't to say that there aren't important benefits to memberships in professional writing organizations; I belong to several.)

But scouring the sources one can find a few poetry prizes that adhere to the fee-free formula. As recommended earlier, be sure to check later portions of *Free Expression* (particularly Multiple/Alternating Genres, Residencies and Retreats, and Student Opportunities) for additional listings that will interest poets.

14
Bordighera Poetry Prize
Sonia Raisziss-Giop Charitable Foundation
c/o Daniela Gioseffi and Alfredo de Palchi
Founders
Box 8G
57 Montague Street
Brooklyn Heights, NY 11201-3356
http://www.italianamericanwriters.com/Prize.html
Deadline: May 31 (postmarked)

Prize provides publication—in bilingual English/Italian edition—for work by an American poet of Italian descent, "to be translated upon selection by the judges into quality translations of modern Italian, for the benefit of American poets of Italian ancestry and the preservation of the Italian language." Cash awards of $1,000 also go the winning poet and to a commissioned translator. Poet must be a U.S. citizen; translator may be an Italian native speaker and need not be a U.S. citizen. Submission may be made in English only or bilingually. "The final book manuscript should not exceed 48 pages since, including translations, the published, bilingual book will be 96 pages in length." Poets should submit two copies of 10 sample pages of poetry (in English). See website for specific manuscript preparation instructions.

15
Cave Canem Poetry Prize
PO Box 4286
Charlottesville, VA 22905-4286
Tel. 434.979.8825
cavecanempoets@aol.com
http://www.cavecanempoets.org/pages/prize.html#guidelines
Deadline: May 15 (postmarked)

Since 1999, this prize has supported "the work of African American poets with excellent manuscripts who have not yet found a publisher for their first book." Prize includes $500 cash, publication of the winner's manuscript by a national press, and 50 copies of the book. Past competitions have also included public readings featuring both contest winner and judge. See website for manuscript submission instructions.

16
Foley Poetry Contest
America
106 West 56th Street
New York, NY 10019-3803
Tel. 212.581.4640
america@americamagazine.org
http://www.americamagazine.org/poetry.cfm
Submissions: January 1-third Friday of April (in 2004: April 16) (received)

Poets may submit one poem of 30 lines or fewer. "Only typed, unpublished poems not under consideration elsewhere will be considered." Entrants must clearly note "Foley Poetry Contest" on the envelope containing the poem. Winning poem is awarded cash prize of $1,000 and publication in *America*. The magazine publishes runners-up and does not accept unsolicited poems for publication outside those sent for the contest.

17
James Laughlin Award
Academy of American Poets
Ryan Murphy, Awards Coordinator
588 Broadway
Suite 604
New York, NY 10012-3210
Tel. 212.274.0343
rmurphy@poets.org

http://www.poets.org/awards/jl_guide.cfm
Note: the James Laughlin guidelines are updated each
year; the following information pertains to the 2003
guidelines.
Submissions: January 1-May 15 (postmarked)

Intended for manuscripts already under contract with
publishers (publishers must send manuscript copies and
entry form). Recognizes a second book of poetry. "To be
eligible, a poet must have published one book of poetry in
a standard edition." Winning poet receives $5,000 and
the Academy agrees to purchase at least 10,000 copies of
the book for distribution to its membership.

18
Naomi Long Madgett Poetry Award
Lotus Press, Inc.
Constance Withers, Assistant to the Editor
P.O. Box 21607
Detroit, MI 48221
Tel. 313.861.1280
lotuspress@aol.com
Submissions: April 1-June 1

Open to African American poets, "whether previously
published or not," although poets "who have worked over
a period of years at developing their craft will have the
best chance for consideration." Award includes a $500
cash prize and publication of the manuscript by Lotus
Press. Writers who have already had a book published by
Lotus Press are ineligible, but inclusion in a Lotus Press
anthology does not disqualify a potential entrant from
submitting to this competition. Poetry manuscript should

total "approximately 60-80 pages, exclusive of a table of contents or other optional introductory material. Begin each poem on a new page, no matter how short it may be, and number the pages." Extensive manuscript preparation and submission guidelines available by SASE, phone, or e-mail—not on the website. Note: guidelines for 2004 competition will be available in January.

19
Thomas Merton Poetry of the Sacred Contest
Thomas Merton Foundation
2117 Payne Street
Louisville, KY 40206
Tel. 502.899.1991/800.886.7275
Fax 502.899.1907 (fax)
info@mertonfoundation.org
http://www.mertonfoundation.org
Deadline: December 31

Offers cash awards ($500 first prize and three Honorable Mentions of $50 each) and publication in *The Merton Seasonal* and online on the Merton Foundation website for poems judged on "literary excellence, spiritual tenor, and human authenticity." See website for submission guidelines, which include a fax option.

20
Andrés Montoya Poetry Prize
Andrés Montoya Poetry Prize
Francisco Aragón, Coordinator
Institute for Latino Studies
230 McKenna Hall

University of Notre Dame
Notre Dame, IN 46556
Tel. 574.631.2882
faragon@nd.edu
http://www.nd.edu/~latino/poetry_prize
Deadline: January 10 (postmarked)

Co-sponsored by the Institute for Latino Studies and the Creative Writing Program at the University of Notre Dame, this competition is open to any Latino/a poet "who has yet to publish a full-length book of poems." Awards a $1000 prize and publication by University of Notre Dame Press. Call or write for further information.

CHAPTER FOUR
Nonfiction

Here, again, you'll find a variety of programs: contests and competitions for everything from an essay to a full-length manuscript; grants to assist with research and publication; awards for works-in-progress.
And of course you're encouraged to find even more possibilities to pursue with your nonfiction in the later sections of the book on Multiple/Alternating Genres, Residencies and Retreats, and Student Opportunities.

21
Frank S. and Elizabeth D. Brewer Prize
American Society of Church History
P.O. Box 8517
Red Bank, NJ 07701
Tel. 732.345.1787
ExSec@churchhistory.org
http://www.churchhistory.org/awards.htm
Deadline: November 1 (received)

This $1000 award, limited to first books, is intended to assist a press in publishing a manuscript in church history. Award is presented at the Society's annual meeting.

22
Dactyl Foundation Essay Awards
c/o Victoria N. Alexander
Dactyl Foundation
54 Grand Street
New York, NY 10013
essays@dactyl.org
http://www.dactyl.org/thought/thought.html
"Entries may be submitted at any time."

For published or unpublished essays, submitted by the author or nominated by another person, of any length. $3,000 award "for essays on literary, aesthetic, or cultural theory, [using or] in some way grounded in science." Include a one-page abstract and send via regular mail, with SASE.

23
Gordon W. Dillon/Richard C. Peterson Memorial Essay Prize
American Orchid Society, Inc.
16700 AOS Lane
Delray Beach, FL 33446-4351
Tel. 561.404.2043
Fax 561.404.2045
jmengel@aos.org (Jane Mengel)
www.orchidweb.org
Deadline: November

Each May *Orchids* magazine announces the theme of this contest, which for 2003 was "Family and Friends with Orchids." Winning entry, "if any," receives a certificate, publication in *Orchids*, and a cash prize ("equaling the interest on an endowment established by the Northeast Judging Center"). Essays should not exceed 5000 words. Deadline in 2003 was November 28; contact Jane Mengel by phone, fax, or e-mail for additional guidelines/information.

24
Dixon Ryan Fox Manuscript Prize

Attn: Daniel H. Goodwin, Editor
New York History
New York State Historical Association
P.O. Box 800
Lake Road
Cooperstown, NY 13326
Tel. 607.547.1491
goodwind@nysha.org
http://www.nysha.org/publications/fox_prize.htm
Deadline: January 20

Annual award for the "best unpublished, book-length monograph dealing with some aspect of the history of New York State." Manuscripts may include biographies and accounts "dealing with such culture matters as literature and the arts, provided that in such cases the methodology is historical." Fiction and works of article length are not eligible. The prize includes a $3,000 award and "assistance with publication." No application form— applicants should sent two unbound copies and a cover letter to Daniel H. Goodwin at the address above.

25
Gantz-Zahler Grant for Jewish Non-Fiction Publishing
National Foundation for Jewish Culture
330 7th Avenue
21st Floor
New York, NY 10001
Tel. 212.629.0500
nfjc@jewishculture.org
http://www.jewishculture.org/grants/gantz_zahler_grant.html
Deadline: October 15

This $2500 grant supports publication of a non-fiction work "reflecting on Jewish life, history, tradition, thought or culture." Proposal package must include a publishing contract. See website for further details and forms. NB: This is a biennial award and the October 15 deadline refers to October 15, 2003.

26
The Humanist Essay Contest
1777 T Street, NW
Washington DC 20009-7125
Tel. 202.238.9088
info@thehumanist.org
http://www.thehumanist.org/essaycontest.html
Deadline: postmarked *before* December 1 each year

For those under the age of 25 who "have thoughts on humanity and the future." Awards a first prize ($1,000), second prize ($400) and third prize ($100). Honorable Mention winners receive certificates. Manuscripts should be under 2500 words. See guidelines for suggested topics. Two notes: this contest administers categories for writers ages 13-17 and 18-24, with ages determined as of the entry deadline of December 1 each contest year. "If you cite a teacher, librarian, dean, or other education adviser (with mailing address) as instrumental to your having entered an essay, and if you are a winner, that individual will be recognized with a special award of $50."

27
H. Earle Johnson Bequest for Book Publication Subvention
Society for American Music
Attn. Maja Trochimczyk
University of Southern California
Thornton School of Music
840 W. 34th Street
Los Angeles, CA 90089-0851
polmusic@usc.edu
http://www.american-music.org
Deadline: "Applications may be made at any time, but applicants should anticipate a long waiting period."
Applicants are advised that in order to ensure consideration before a relevant Board meeting, "applications should be received by the date set by the committee. Currently that date is November 15."

Intended "to support the costs of the publication of a significant monograph on an important topic in American Music," this award provides two subventions up to $2,500 each year. A publisher must already have agreed to publish the work. Applicants must send six copies of application materials, which should include a statement about the publication plans, a detailed financial statement, a brief curriculum vita, outline of proposed publication, and sample chapter or excerpt. See website for details.

28
J. Anthony Lukas Work-in-Progress Award
Lukas Prize Project
Columbia University Graduate School of Journalism
2950 Broadway MC 3800
New York, NY 10027
Tel. 212.854.8653
lukas@jrn.columbia.edu
http://www.jrn.columbia.edu
Deadline: December 12

An award of $45,000, open to writers who already have publishing contracts for a nonfiction book. Applicants must send copies of original book proposal, sample chapter, proof of publishing contract, and description of how award will help with the book's progress. Entry form available on website.

29
National Library of Medicine Publication Grant Program
Attn. Valerie Florance, Ph.D.
Extramural Programs
National Library of Medicine
Rockledge 1, Suite 301
6705 Rockledge Drive
Bethesda, MD 20892

Tel. 301.594.4882
floranv@mail.nlm.nih.gov
http://www.nlm.nih.gov/pubs/factsheets/pubgrant.html
Thrice-annual deadlines: February 1, June 1, October 1

Awards grants "to provide short-term assistance for the preparation of book-length manuscripts about information of value to U.S. health professionals." Projects include "major critical reviews, historical studies, and current developments in informatics, technology, librarianship, and secondary reference materials in the biomedical field." Grant application form available on website.

30
PEN/Jerard Fund Award
PEN American Center
568 Broadway
New York, NY 10012-3225
awards@pen.org
http://www.pen.org/awards/jerard.htm
Deadline: January 6 (2005)

This biennial cash prize—$5500 in 2001 and 2003—is awarded to a woman writer "at an early point in her career." The prize recognizes "a work in progress of general nonfiction distinguished by high literary quality." Although applicants "must not have published more than one book of any kind," they should have published "at least one magazine article in a national publication or in a major literary magazine." See website for detailed award description and application guidelines, which include the submission of two copies of no more than 50 pages of the work in progress accompanied by list of applicant's publications.

31
Barbara Savage "Miles from Nowhere" Award
The Mountaineers Books
1001 SW Klickitat Way
Suite 201
Seattle, WA 98134
Tel. 206.223.6303
mbooks@mountaineersbooks.org
http://www.mountaineersbooks.org/mtn_b_savage_awar
d.cfm
Deadline: March 1 (received)

A memorial award honoring Barbara Savage, whose *Miles from Nowhere* chronicled the two-year, 25,000-mile round-the-world bicycle trip she and her husband Larry shared, this prize offers a $3,000 cash award, a $12,000 advance against royalties, and publication by The Mountaineers Books. "The winning manuscript will be a compelling non-fiction account of a personal outdoor adventure." See website for further details on subject matter and submission guidelines.

32
Society Research Fellowships
Wisconsin Historical Society
816 State Street
Madison, WI 53706
Tel. 608.264.6463 (Kate Thompson—book projects)
Tel. 608.264.6549 (Margaret Dwyer—article projects)

http://www.wisconsinhistory.org/research/fellowships.ht
ml
Quarterly deadlines: "Applications are accepted year
round, but are evaluated in January, April, July, and
October."

These awards (the D.C. Everest, John C. Geilfuss, Amy
Louise Hunter, and Alice E. Smith Fellowships) support
research and writing with the goal of publication either in
the *Wisconsin Magazine of History* "or in book form by the
society. "Eligible individual applicants include
"professional and nonprofessional writers, academics, and
independent scholars." Grants "usually are between $500
and $1,000 for an article-length work and between
$1,500 to $3,000 for a book-length work." Note that the
Wisconsin Historical Society of Wisconsin Press "has the
right of first refusal for any manuscripts developed with
these awards. See guidelines for specific subject
requirements for each award and for application forms.

33
Edward H. Tihen Historical Publication Award
Kansas State Historical Society
Attn. Virgil W. Dean
6425 SW Sixth Avenue
Topeka, KS 66615
Tel. 785.272.8681
vdean@kshs.org
http://www.kshs.org/involved/help/tihen.htm#publication
Deadline: July 1

"Promotes the publication of material on the history of
Kansas by first-time authors." Total grant funds available:

$750, though no single award may exceed $500. Note: research grants are also available, for "non-academic researchers." See website for guidelines for these grants, which have an application deadline of April 1.

34
U.S. Naval Institute Arleigh Burke Essay Contest
U.S. Naval Institute
291 Wood Road
Annapolis, MD 21402-5034
Tel. 410.295.1058
bjudge@usni.org
http://www.usni.org/membership/CONTESTS.htm#essay
Deadline: December 1 (postmarked)

Open to all writers addressing the goal of the Naval Institute: "to provide an open forum for those who dare to read, think, speak and write in order to advance professional, literary, and scientific understanding of sea power and other issues critical to national security." Cash prizes ($3,000 first prize, $2,000 second prize, $1,000 third prize) and publication in the professional magazine, *Proceedings*. Winners also receive membership in the Naval Institute (the first prize winner is awarded a lifetime membership). Gold, silver, and bronze medals are also awarded. Essays may be submitted electronically or via postal mail. See website for detailed submission/manuscript guidelines and information on other writing and photography contests.

35
Writer's Digest Chronicle
Online submission through website. "No faxed or snail mail entries, please."
http://www.writersdigest.com/contests/your_chronicle_display.asp
Deadline: the 25th of each month

This competition welcomes personal essays on writing challenges and triumphs and awards a monthly prize of $125 and online publication, with possible print publication. Essays that do not win in one submission cycle may be resubmitted; multiple submissions are also acceptable. "Be aware that we are overloaded with entries about writing experiences from childhood, teachers who have influenced your writing, battling writer's block, and entries praising *Writer's Digest*. Please try to make your entry stand out from the others by avoiding these topics unless you have an extraordinary story."

CHAPTER FIVE
Plays

You'll find here a sampling of competitions that lead to staging of unpublished plays. As with other literary competitions, some of these programs require separate cover sheets and/or entry forms to ensure fair judging and may ask that the work itself not bear the writer's name. Binding instructions may vary by competition as well. Again, be sure to read each competition's guidelines very carefully.

And, again, for additional ideas please consult the opportunities in the sections on Multiple/Alternating Genres and Residencies and Retreats.

36
Beverly Hills Theatre Guild/Julie Harris Playwright Awards Competition
Dick Dotterer, Competition Coordinator
P.O. Box 39729
Los Angeles, CA 90039-0729
http://www.beverlyhillstheatreguild.org/jhrules.htm
Submissions: August 1-November 1 (postmarked)

"To discover new theatrical works and to encourage established or emerging quality works for the theatre." Competition awards a first prize (June Moray Playwright Award) of $5,000; a second prize (the Janet and Maxwell Salter Playwright Award) of $2,500; and a third prize (the Dr. Henry and Lilian Nesburm Playwright Award) of

$1,500. Plays must be full-length (at least 90 minutes playing time), unpublished, unproduced, and not currently under any option. Musicals, adaptations, translations, plays for children, plays that have previously won other competitions or previously been entered in the Beverly Hills Theatre Guild Playwright Award Competition are not eligible. Entrants may submit only one entry. Entries must include application form, which is available by sending SASE to the Competition Coordinator, and must be submitted according to the competition's specific policies.

37
Clayton State Theater Prize for Playwriting
c/o Ed Holbein
Clayton College and State University
5900 North Lee Street
Morrow, GA 30260
Tel. 770.961.3460
edholbein@mail.clayton.edu
http://a-s.clayton.edu/cstheater/PlayWritingContest/
Deadline: November 15 (received)

Established in 2003 by retired Clayton State Theater Artistic Director Dr. Larry Corse, this award (open in 2003 only to Georgia residents but expected to open nationwide in the future) provides $1,000 and the opportunity to have one's play staged by Clayton State Theater. Submitted plays must be "original, in English, non-musical, and must not have been performed or published previously." Submissions may be either full-length, one-act, or a series of related one-act plays. Running time should be between 90 and 120 minutes and no more than six actors should be needed. Contact Ed Holbein for details.

38
Siena College International Playwrights
Competition and New York City Showcase
Siena College
515 Loudon Road
Loudonville, NY 12211-1462
Tel. 518.783.2300
http://www.siena.edu/theatre/playwrights.htm
Submissions: February 1-June 30 (postmarked)

For previously unproduced, unpublished scripts. Award includes cash prize of $2,000 plus expenses for a campus residency, during which the playwright "will participate in rehearsals, design conferences, public discussions and the academic life of the Siena Community." Scripts should be full-length, featuring 3-10 actors. "The age range of the ensemble should be suitable for undergraduate performers" and the play should "require a unit set or minimal set changes." An application form required and is available on the website. The Siena production will be remounted in New York City.

39
Southeastern Theatre Conference/Charles M.
Getchell New Play Award
PO Box 9868
Greensboro, NC 27429
Tel. 336.272.3645

(note—this is the SETC contact information; Play Award materials are submitted elsewhere)
http://www.setc.org/scholarship/newplay.html
Submissions: March 1-June 1

Awards $1,000 and a staged reading, plus paid travel and room and board to attend the annual Southeastern Theatre Conference convention. Submissions must be unproduced and unpublished full-length plays or programs of two related one-acts. No musicals or children's plays. "Students and playwrights residing in or studying at an accredited college in the SETC member region are eligible for consideration." Member states include: Alabama, Florida, Georgia, Kentucky, Mississippi, North Carolina, South Carolina, Tennessee, Virginia, West Virginia. Application form required.

40
Southern Playwrights Competition
c/o Stephanie Kirby
Department of English
Jacksonville State University
700 Pelham Road north
Jacksonville, AL 36365-1602
Tel. 256.782.5411
skirby@jsucc.jsu.edu
swhitton@jsucc.jsu.edu
http://www.jsu.edu/depart/english/southpla.htm
Submissions: September 1-February 15 (received)

Annual award of $1000, and production by the Jacksonville State University Department of Drama, to winning playwright, who must be native to or resident of

Alabama, Arkansas, Florida, Georgia, Kentucky, Louisiana, Mississippi, North Carolina, South Carolina, Tennessee, Texas, Virginia, or West Virginia. "Plays must deal with the Southern experience." Plays must be original and full-length; no musicals or adaptations. Entry form required.

CHAPTER SIX
Children's Literature

Here are a few opportunities not for writing *by* children or young adults, but for writing *for* them.

41
Marguerite de Angeli Contest
Delacorte Press/Random House, Inc.
1745 Broadway
New York, NY 10019
Tel. 212.782.9000
http://www.randomhouse.com/kids/games/marguerite.ht
ml
Submissions: April 1-June 30 (postmarked)

Named for the children's book author and illustrator of 28 works that received honors including the Newbery Medal, two Caledcott Honor Awards, the Lewis Carroll Shelf Award, and the Regina Medal, this contest awards a book contract for a hardcover and a paperback edition "to encourage the writing of contemporary or historical fiction set in North America, for readers age 8-12." Prize consists of $1,500 and $7,500 advance against royalties. U.S. and Canadian writers who have not previously published novels for middle-grade readers are eligible. Manuscripts may not be submitted elsewhere while under consideration for this prize.

42
Association of Jewish Libraries Sydney Taylor Manuscript Award
c/o Rachel K. Glasser
315 Maitland Avenue
Teaneck, NJ 07666
rkglasser@aol.com
http://www.jewishlibraries.org/ajlweb/awardsscholarships
_files/taylor_mss.htm
Deadline: December 1

For aspiring authors of Jewish children's books, this award recognizes the best fiction manuscript appropriate for readers ages 8-11, written by an unpublished author. $1,000 prize. Application form is required and is available on the website.

43
Delacorte Press Contest for a First Young Adult Novel
Random House, Inc.
1745 Broadway, 9th Floor
New York, NY 10019
Tel. 212.782.9000
http://www.randomhouse.com/kids/games/delacorte.htm
l
Submissions: October 1-December 31 (postmarked)

This contest promotes contemporary young adult fiction. Award includes $1,500 cash, $7,500 advance against royalties, and publication in hardcover and paperback editions. Manuscript may not be submitted elsewhere while under consideration for this prize.

44
Highlights for Children Fiction Contest
803 Church Street
Honesdale, PA 18431
Tel. 570.253.1080
http://www.highlights.com
Submissions: January   1-February   29   (2004)
(postmarked)

For 2004, the fiction contest welcomes stories up to 800 words "that begin with the words 'I have a problem.'" Note that "beginning reader" stories should be 500 words, maximum. "No crime, violence, or derogatory humor." Three prizes of $1,000 each; winning stories will be published in *Highlights*. No entry form.

45
Ezra Jack Keats/Kerlan Collection
Memorial Fellowship
113 Andersen Library
222 21st Avenue South
University of Minnesota
Minneapolis, MN 55455
Tel. 612.624.4576
clrc@tc.umn.edu
http://special.lib.umn.edu/clrc/awards.html#2
Deadline: May 1 (postmarked)

Fellowship from the Ezra Jack Keats Foundation provides $1500 to a "talented writer and/or illustrator of children's books who wishes to use the Kerlan Collection for the furtherance of his or her artistic development." Contact the Ezra Jack Keats/Kerlan Collection Memorial Fellowship

for application materials (send a large (6"X9" or 9"X12")
self-addressed envelope with $.55 postage.

46
Lee & Low Books New Voices Award
95 Madison Avenue
New York, NY 10016
Tel. 212.779.4400
info@leeandlow.com
http://www.leeandlow.com/editorial/voices.html
Submissions: April 1-October 31 (postmarked)

For a children's picture book story by a writer of color
who has not previously published a children's picture
book. Cash grant of $1,000 and standard publication
contract. Honor award winner receives cash grant of
$500. Submissions may be works of fiction or nonfiction
intended for children ages 2-10. "Folklore and animal
stories will not be considered." Manuscripts should be a
maximum of 1500 words and should address the needs of
children of color by providing stories with which they can
identify and relate, and which promote a greater
understanding of one another. Of special interest are
stories in contemporary settings." Entrants may submit
up to two manuscripts, though each submission should be
sent separately. Submission guidelines available on the
website.

47
Milkweed Prize for Children's Literature
Milkweed Editions
Open Book Building

Suite 300
1011 Washington Avenue South
Minneapolis, MN 55415-1246
Tel. 612.332.3192/800.520.6455
webmaster@milkweed.org
http://www.milkweed.org

This prize is awarded to the best novel manuscript, intended for readers 8-13 years of age, that Milkweed accepts for publication during the calendar year by an author who has not been previously published by Milkweed. All manuscripts submitted to Milkweed are considered for the prize, which includes a $10,000 cash advance "on any royalties agreed upon in the contractual arrangement negotiated at the time of acceptance." Submissions must follow the guidelines for children's literature submissions to Milkweed. Picture books and story collections are ineligible. "Milkweed Editions is looking for manuscripts of high literary quality that embody humane values and contribute to cultural understanding."

48
Pockets Fiction-Writing Contest
Upper Room
Pockets/Lynn W. Gilliam
1908 Grand Ave.
P.O. Box 340004
Nashville, TN 37203-0004
pockets@upperroom.org
http://courtyard.upperroom.org/pockets/contest.html
Submissions: March 1-August 15 (postmarked)

Welcomes stories of 1000-1600 words according to requirements similar to those for regularly submitted material, so be sure to consult the website for helpful guidance here. Winner receives a $1,000 award and publication in Pockets, a magazine designed for 6-12 year olds that "offers wholesome devotional readings that teach about God's love and presence in life."

CHAPTER SEVEN
Multiple/Alternating Genres

Some programs alternate their awards—fiction writers may be their focus one year, while only poets are eligible another. Or arts councils may award grants to literary artists in one fiscal year and visual artists the next. Other programs may always welcome submissions in more than one literary genre.

Of course, you should also be sure to check the genre-specific sections throughout *Free Expression* (fiction, poetry, nonfiction, playwriting, children's literature) for additional possibilities to pursue in your literary field. And then read the next chapter, on residencies and retreats, conferences and colonies....

49
Alaska State Council on the Arts Career Opportunity Grants
Alaska State Council on the Arts
411 West 4th Avenue, Suite 1E
Anchorage, AK 99501-2343
Tel. 907.269.6610/1.888.278.7424
aksca_info@eed.state.ak.us
http://www.educ.state.ak.us/aksca/
Monthly deadlines: "Applications must be postmarked or received in the Council office (by the close of business) on the first day of the month prior to the month of your planned career opportunity. For example: if the activity

begins March 15, the application must be postmarked or received by February 1."

These grants are intended to assist writers and other professional artists "for travel to in-state, national, or international events, programs or seminars; and for other activities that will contribute to the strength of the applicant's professional standing or skill." Grants usually are less than $1,000. Applicants must be at least 18 years of age at time of applicants, must be Alaska residents, must not be enrolled as a full-time student during the period of the grant, and may only win Career Opportunity Grants every other state fiscal year. Entry form required.

50
Bush Artist Fellows Program
Kathi Polley, Program Assistant
East 900
First National Bank Building
332 Minnesota Street
St. Paul, MN 55101
Tel. 651.227.0891/1.800.605.7315
kpolley@bushfoundation.org
http://www.bushfoundation.org
Deadline: check for 2005 Literature Fellowship deadlines; 2004 deadlines were in October 2003

Through the Archibald Bush Foundation, this program offers a number of $44,000 grants to applicants who propose fellowship plans lasting 12-24 continuous months. Grant categories rotate on a two-year cycle; 2005 fellowships will include literature (poetry, fiction, and non-fiction) and scriptworks ("for stage and screen"). Applicants must be U.S. citizens or permanent residents, at least 25 years of age, and residents of Minnesota, North Dakota, South Dakota, or one of 26 counties in northwestern Wisconsin listed in the fellowship guidelines who have lived in one of these states "for at least 12 of the 36 months preceding the application deadline." Contact the Foundation for a printed Fellowship Application, or download from the website.

51
Chicano/Latino Literary Prize
University of California, Irvine
Department of Spanish and Portuguese
322 Humanities Hall
Irvine, CA 92697-5275
Tel. 949.824.5443
cllp@uci.edu
http://www.hnet.uci.edu/spanishandportuguese/cllp/main_novel.htm
Deadline: June 1 (postmarked)

Each year the call for entries is genre-specific. In 2004, short story collections (minimum of 175 double-spaced, typed pages) will be welcome; in 2005, poetry collections. First place winner receives $1000, publication "if not under previous contract," and transportation to Irvine to receive the award. The second place winner receives $500 and the third place winner receives $250. See website for detailed submission guidelines.

52
Martin Dibner Fellowship for Maine Writers
Maine Community Foundation
Attn. Jean Warren/Carl Little
245 Main St.
Ellsworth, ME 04605
Tel. 207.667.9735/1.877.700.6800
jwarren@mainecf.org/clittle@mainecf.org
http://www.mainecf.org/html/grants/available/martin.ht
ml
Deadline: May 15 (received)

A grant of $500-$1000, for Maine writers, "to allow them to further their writing skills and experience. Attendance at writing workshops is the primary purpose for support, and secondarily for assistance with living expenses while finishing a writing project." In even years, the award is directed to fiction writers; in odd years, to poets. Application should include a statement of the applicant's objectives, a one-page summary of the project, a budget, a resume that lists previously published works, a writing sample (5-7 single-sided pages, with a separate page listing applicant's name, address, phone and title of submission).

53
Glasgow Prize for Emerging Writers
c/o R.T. Smith
Shenandoah
Mattingly House
Washington and Lee University
Lexington, VA 24450-0303
Tel. 540.463.8908.

http://shenandoah.wlu.edu/glasgow.html
Submissions: February 1-March 31

Prize includes cash award ($2500), publication of new work in *Shenandoah*, and a reading at Washington and Lee University. 2004 prize is open to writers of poetry with only one published book in that genre; 2005 prize will be for creative nonfiction; 2006 prize will be awarded to the author of a short story collection. Applicants must send first books, samples of new work (up to five unpublished poems) and vita for consideration.

54
Kishor M. Kulkarni Arts and Humanities Prize on Modern India
India Studies Program
Indiana University
Sycamore Hall 334
Bloomington, IN 47405-7005
Tel. 812.855.4848
http://www.indiana.edu/~isp/kulkarni.shtml
Deadline: February 28

Open to permanent residents and citizens of the United States 18-35 years of age who are descendants of citizens of the region now known as the Republic of India. One $2,500 award will be given although submissions will be accepted in three categories: "analytic," "creative," and "cinema/video." See website for full guidelines and required entry form.

55
Leeway Foundation Window of Opportunity (WOO) Grants
Pam Shropshire, Program Director
123 South Broad Street
Suite 2040
Philadelphia, PA 19109
Tel. 215.545.4078
info@leeway.org
http://www.leeway.org
Deadlines: 4X/year (in 2003, deadlines fell in January, April, June and November)

Awards grants of up to $2,000 to support women artists working in any discipline, 20 years of age or older, who currently reside in Bucks, Chester, Delaware, Montgomery or Philadelphia county in the Commonwealth of Pennsylvania. Applicants must have already obtained a commitment from "a recognized institution, organization or mentor" for the proposed project. Window of Opportunity Grants support opportunities such as "[t]ravel associated with an imminent, concrete opportunity" (such as a book tour or residency); chances for "advanced study with a significant mentor (not degree-related)"; equipment purchase. Application forms are required. See the website/contact the Leeway Foundation for further information.

56
Malice Domestic Grants for Unpublished Writers
William L. Starck, Grants Chair
Malice Domestic, Ltd.
P.O. Box 31137

Bethesda, MD 20824-1137
grants@malicedomestic.org
http://www.malicedomestic.org/grants.htm
Submissions: September 15-December 15 (received)

The genre of "Malice Domestic," according to the website, is "loosely described as mystery stories of the Agatha Christie type—i.e. 'traditional mysteries'. These works usually feature an amateur detective, characters who know each other, and no excessive gore, gratuitous violence, or explicit sex." Each of two grants includes $1,000 plus registration fee and lodging for (but not transportation to) the Malice Domestic Convention. Grants are intended "to offset registration, travel, or other expenses related to attendance at a writers' conference or workshop within a year of the date of the award...In the case of nonfiction, the grant may be used to offset research expenses." See website for detailed guidelines.

57
MVP (Many Voices Project)
New Rivers Press
Minnesota State University-Moorhead
1104 7th Ave. S.
Moorhead, MN 56563
Tel. 218.477.5870
nrp@mnstate.edu
http://www.newriverspress.com
Submissions: October 1-November 30

Open to "emerging writers of poetry, short fiction, novels, novellas, personal essays, memoirs, and other forms of creative prose." Book publication is awarded to three writers—in 2003 one manuscript was selected from a nationwide pool and two from writers resident in either Minnesota or New York City. Required entry form.

58
William Morris Society Fellowship
William Morris Society in the United States
P.O. Box 53263
Washington, DC 20009
http://www.morrissociety.org/fellowships.html
Deadline: September 1

Each year up to $1,000 is granted to individuals for expenses associated with projects "relating to Morris." Projects "may be scholarly or creative in nature." Applicants "need not have an academic or institutional appointment, and the Ph.D. is not required." Applications must include a resume, a one-page proposal, and two letters of recommendation (those letters should be sent separately).

59
New Hampshire State Council on the Arts Individual Artist Fellowship
Julie Mento, Artist Services Coordinator
2 1/2 Beacon Street—2nd Floor
Concord, NH 03301-4974
Tel. 603.271.0790
jmento@nharts.state.nh.us
http://www.nh.gov/nharts/grantsandservices/
Deadline: May 7 (postmarked)

Recognizing "artistic excellence and professional commitment," a fellowship "does not have to be used for a specific project. Past fellowships have been used "to upgrade studios, travel, purchase new computers, take unpaid leaves from jobs to focus on [one's] art form, and experiment with new media." Up to six $5,000 awards are offered to artists who are over 18 years of age; resident in New Hampshire at time of application, having lived in the state for one year prior to application and planning to live in New Hampshire for the fellowship year; with resumes and work samples demonstrating professional commitment to their artistic discipline. See website for full guidelines, instructions, and required form.

60
Ohioana Walter Rumsey Marvin Grant
Ohioana Library Association
274 E. First Ave.
Suite 300
Columbus, OH 43201
Contact: Linda Hengst
Tel. 614.466.3831
ohioana@sloma.state.oh.us
http://www.oplin.lib.oh.us/index.cfm?id=773-775
Deadline: January 31 (postmarked)

Established by the family of a former Director of the Ohioana Library Association, this grant is a $1,000 award given to a writer under 30 years of age who has not yet published a book. The candidate must have been born in Ohio or have lived in Ohio for a minimum of five years. Entries (up to six prose pieces) must total no more than 60 pages; 10 pages minimum. Required entry form "or a letter from the applicant containing: her/her date and place of birth; dates and place of residence in Ohio, and a statement that the applicant has not published a book."

61
PeaceWriting International Writing Awards
2582 Jimmie
Fayetteville, AR 72703-3420
Tel. 501.442.4600
jbennet@comp.uark.edu
Deadline: December 1 (postmarked)

Seeking full-length, unpublished book manuscripts "about the causes, consequences, and solutions to violence and war, and about the ideas and practices of nonviolent peacemaking the lives of nonviolent peacemakers," these prizes award $500 to the winning manuscript in each of three categories: non-fiction ("history, biography, political science, international law, etc."); imaginative work ("novel, short stories, poems, play"); work for young people ("non-fiction or imaginative"). Plays must not have been professionally produced. Entrants may submit more than one manuscript. Manuscripts should be "securely bound and clearly typed, double-spaced; front and back of pages allowed." The author's name should not appear on the manuscript, but the following information should be included separately: one-page synopsis of the manuscript, one-paragraph biography of the writer, and author's name and address. Send SASE for full guidelines.

62
Pew Fellowships in the Arts
230 South Broad Street
Suite 1003
Philadelphia, PA 19102
Tel. 215.875.2285
pewarts@mindspring.com
http://www.pewarts.org
Deadline: December 1

Awards grants of $50,000 directly to artists "so that they may have the opportunity to dedicate themselves to creative pursuits exclusively." Artists must be "verifiable Pennsylvania residents of Bucks, Chester, Delaware, Montgomery, or Philadelphia County for two years or longer immediately prior to the application deadline" and must maintain residence in this area throughout the selection process; those granted fellowships must maintain residence in the area during the fellowship period. Fellowships are awarded in twelve disciplines that rotate on a four-year cycle; check with PFA for current disciplines under review; for 2004 these included folk and traditional arts, painting, and scriptworks.

63
Mary Roberts Rinehart Awards
English Department, George Mason University
MSN 3E4
Fairfax, VA 22030-4444
Tel. 703.993.1180
bgompert@gmu(Barb Gomperts)
http://www.gmu.edu/departments/writing/rinehart.htm
Deadline: November 30 (postmarked)

Annual grants to recognize unpublished works "by writers who have not yet published a book or whose writing is not regularly appearing in nationally circulated commercial or literary magazines." Writers must be nominated "by someone in the field—another writer, an agent, an editor or the like." Three grants of $2,000 each are awarded for best manuscripts in fiction, in nonfiction, and in poetry. Fiction and nonfiction entries should be "freestanding" and should not exceed 30 pages; poetry submissions should include 10 pages of individual or collected poems. Entry packets include the nominating letter, two copies of the manuscript, and a brief autobiographical statement. Mark genre on the envelope.

64
San Francisco Foundation/Jackson and Phelan Literary Awards
c/o Intersection for the Arts
466 Valencia Street
San Francisco, CA 94103
Att: Cedric Brown
clb@sff.org
http://www.sff.org
Deadline: January 31

Supports "young writers of unpublished manuscripts in progress." Applicants must be 20-35 years of age as of the application deadline (January 31). Three awards are available: the $2,000 Joseph Henry Jackson Literary Award recognizes a resident of northern California/ Nevada whose work may be fiction, nonfiction prose, or poetry; the James Duval Phelan Award recognizes a

California native (not necessarily a current resident) with a $2,000 award also for a work-in-progress of fiction, nonfiction prose, or poetry—but drama submissions are also welcome. The Tenenbaum Award for Nonfiction, also for $2,000, goes to a northern California resident specializing in nonfiction prose.

65
South Dakota Arts Council Artist Grant
Office of Arts
800 Governors Drive
Pierre, SD 57501-2294
Tel. 605.773.3131
sdac@stlib.state.sd.us
http://www.sdarts.org
Deadline: March 1 (postmarked)

Grants of $3,000 are made to South Dakota artists (resident in the state for at least two years prior to application) for purposes including but not limited to: "to set aside time to pursue their work, to purchase materials and equipment, to produce in new work, aid in the marketing or promotion of a specific project, or reach new audiences for existing work." Required form.

66
Woodford Reserve Series in Kentucky Literature
Sarabande Books, Inc.
2234 Dundee Road, Suite 200
Louisville, KY 40205
Tel. 502.458.4028
http://www.sarabandebooks.org

Submissions: Materials must be postmarked during the month of July. "No exceptions."

Each year Sarabande Books publishes one book of short stories, poetry, or creative nonfiction, or a novella(s) or short novel written by an author a) who is a native of Kentucky or b) who has lived in Kentucky for at least five years or c) whose manuscript is set in Kentucky or d) whose manuscript is about Kentucky. See the website for additional guidelines for this series, and other publishing opportunities with Sarabande.

CHAPTER EIGHT
Residencies and Retreats, Conferences and Colonies

Particularly as we advance in our work as writers, we're likely to seek those especially rewarding—and remunerative—opportunities that we often know as Residencies and Retreats. These plums, often involving fellowships and sojourns at conferences and colonies, can offer stipends, lodging, and other benefits—not to mention the potentially priceless prizes of writing time, access to research collections and/or connections with other writers.

67
American Antiquarian Society Fellowships for Creative and Performing Artists and Writers
James Moran, Director of Outreach
185 Salisbury Street
Worcester, MA 01609-1634
Tel. 508.471.2131/471.2139
jmoran@mwa.org
http://www.americanantiquarian.org/artistfellowship.htm
Deadline: October 5 (received)

Fellowships provide recipients 4 weeks in residence at the Society and provide for stipend of $1200 and travel expenses, offering recipients "the opportunity for a period of uninterrupted research, reading and collegial discussion." Sample fellowship projects include historical novels, poetry, plays, and magazine and newspaper articles. Consult the website for the application cover sheet and detailed instructions, or contact the AAS for a fellowship application packet.

68
Bernheim Writing Fellowship
P.O. Box 130
Clermont, KY 40110
Tel. 502.955.8512 x247
LaDonna Eastman, Public Relations Coordinator
http://www.bernheim.org/arts.htm#Bernheim%20Writing%20Fellowship%202001
Submissions: October 1-December 31

The Fellow receives "comfortable housing" at the Bernheim Arboretum and Research Forest for up to three months and a grant of up to $1000 to cover travel and other expenses. The Fellow must donate work produced during the Fellowship to the Bernheim Library Collection, and "interact with the public in some way, which may include leading a workshop, readings, book signings, etc. Bernheim will reach an agreement regarding the work to be donated and the interaction required from each artist." Applicants should send five sets of an application package including a resume, fellowship proposal, work sample (ten poems, one play, two short stories, novel excerpts, or essay), and at least one letter of recommendation. "The proposal may or may not be specific but should outline areas that you would like to explore in nature." Applicant's name should not appear on work samples or on the proposal, but may be included in the resume and reference letter. Applications should be sent by certified mail, Federal Express, or UPS Next Day Air.

69
Bread Loaf Writers' Conference
Noreen Cargill, Administrative Manager
Middlebury College
Middlebury, VT 05753
Tel. 802.443.5286
ncargill@middlebury.edu
http://www.middlebury.edu/blwc
Deadline: March 1

Depending on a writer's level of achievement, a variety of fellowships and scholarships can help cover tuition and fees at the Bread Loaf Writers' Conference, held each August. Check the website for application forms and guidelines, or request print copy of the materials.

70
Hodder Fellowship
Council of the Humanities
Joseph Henry House
Princeton University
Princeton, NJ 08544-5264
humcounc@princeton.edu
http://www.princeton.edu/~humcounc
Deadline: November 1 (postmarked)

For "humanists in the early stages of their careers," this fellowship, which for 2004-05 will provide a stipend of $54,000, "is awarded to individuals during that crucial period when they have demonstrated exceptional promise but have not yet received widespread recognition. Typically, Hodder Fellows have published one highly acclaimed book and are undertaking significant new work that might not be possible without the 'studious leisure' afforded by this fellowship." Hodder Fellows live in Princeton for the academic year. Applicants must send résumé, sample of previous work, 2-3 page project proposal, and SASE for acknowledgment.

71
Island Institute Resident Fellows Program
Box 2420
Sitka, AK 99835
Tel. 907.747.3794
island@ak.net
http://home.gci.net/~island/ResidentFellows.html
Deadline: August 15 (for applications for all three residency periods)

Month-long residencies (private apartments and $300 food stipends) provided to poets, fiction writers, and creative nonfiction writers during January, April and November. The Program is intended for writers who are interested in integrating "the perspectives of the humanities, arts, and sciences in ways that recognize community values." Residents are expected to participate in a community activity at least once each week during their stay, including public readings, talks to schools or college classes, writing workshops, group discussions, "or other appropriate events." Downloadable application form and instructions available on the website.

72
Koret Young Writer on Jewish Themes Award
Koret Foundation
33 New Montgomery Street, Suite 1090
San Francisco, CA 94105-4526
Tel. 415.882-7740, ext.3
koretinstitute@koretfoundation.org
http://www.koretfoundation.org/initiatives/young_writer.
shtml
Deadline: December 1

For a writer 35 years of age or under who has published
no more than one book and whose work contains Jewish
themes. Award includes $25,000 and a three-month
residency at Stanford University. The writer teaches one
course at Stanford and gives workshops in collaboration
with local Jewish community organizations. Requires
application coversheet (available on the website) along
with a curriculum vitae (maximum three pages) and a
description of work-in-progress (maximum two pages).
Finalists will be asked to submit manuscripts for review.

73
Ledig House International Writers' Residency
Ledig House Applications
55 Fifth Avenue, 15th Floor
New York, NY 10003
Artomi55@aol.com
http://www.artomi.org/
Deadline: November 30

"Writers and translators from all fields are encouraged to
apply for a residence lasting anywhere from one week to

two months." Ledig House provides all meals. Applications must include a biographical sketch "including publications, performances and writing credits"; a non-returnable copy of "latest published work. If unpublished, send a ten page sample of your latest work"; a one-page description of the work the applicant intends to pursue while at Ledig House; one letter of recommendation; a SASE for notification; telephone number or e-mail address. Applicants are also asked to express a preference for a fall or spring residency. Spring session lasts April 1-June 24; Fall session runs August 24-October 31. "The amount of time desired per session—no shorter than one week and no longer than two months—should also be indicated."

74
Richard J. Margolis Award of Blue Mountain Center
c/o Margolis & Associates
137 Newbury Street, 2nd Floor
Boston, MA 02116
http://www.margolis.com/award
Deadline: July 1

This $5,000 award—plus one month residency at the Blue Mountain Center in Blue Mountain Lake, New York—recognizes "a promising new journalist or essayist whose work combines warmth, humor, wisdom and concern with social justice" and is named for Richard J. Margolis, a journalist, essayist and poet "who gave eloquent voice to the hardships of the rural poor, migrant farm workers, the elderly, Native Americans and others whose voices are seldom heard." Applications should be sent to the above address, and should include at least two examples of the applicant's work (published or unpublished, 30 pages maximum, three sets of copies) and a biographical note with description of current and anticipated work.

75
Philip Roth Residence in Creative Writing
Stadler Center for Poetry
Bucknell Hall
Bucknell University
Lewisburg, PA 17837
Tel. 570.577.1853
stadlercenter@bucknell.edu
http://www.bucknell.edu/StadlerCenter/
Deadline: March 15 (postmarked)

Awarded in alternate years to a poet and a writer of fiction working on a first or second book, this residence at Bucknell University offers an emerging writer lodging in the University's Poet's Cottage, an office in the Stadler Center for Poetry, and a $2,000 stipend. Although the Resident has no formal academic obligations, "it is hoped that he or she will constitute a presence as a working writer on campus, talking informally from time to time with students who are interested in writing." Note: in recent years the residence has been offered in the spring semester but it is now returning to the fall schedule with a corresponding change in 2004 to the March 15 application deadline.

76
Shenandoah International Playwrights Retreat
SHENANARTS
Pennyroyal Farm
717 Quicks Mill Rd.
Staunton, VA 24401
Tel. 540.248.1868
http://www.shenanarts.org
Deadline: February 1 (postmarked)

Full fellowships (room, board, and transportation) "to test and develop new work" are offered for the August Retreat. Awards are based on evaluations of submitted work, which may be plays, musicals, or screenplays. Applications must include two copies of a typed, bound draft of the applicant's proposed project, a personal statement/biographical background of the applicant's experience as a writer, a stamped and self-addressed postcard for receipt acknowledgment, and a SASE for manuscript return (or note stating manuscript return is not desired).

77
Steinbeck Fellows Program
Paul Douglass, Coordinator, Steinbeck Fellows Program
English Department
San Jose State University
San Jose, CA 95192-0090
Tel. 408.924.4425
pdouglas@email.sjsu.edu
http://www2.sjsu.edu/depts/english/Steinbeckfellows.htm
Deadline: April 15

This program, endowed by Professor Emerita Martha Heasley Cox offers "new writers of any age and background the opportunity to pursue a significant project in collaboration with other writers, faculty and graduate students." Program includes a one-year fellowship in Steinbeck scholarship and at least one fellowship in creative writing. "Fellows may be appointed in many fields, including literary scholarship, fiction, drama, education, science, and the media. The genre of poetry, however, is excluded." Fellowship stipend: $7,500. "Housing assistance available." Application should include a resume, prospectus of the work to be written (maximum three pages), a writing sample (maximum thirty pages), three letters of recommendation, three additional references or contacts, and a self-addressed envelope.

78
E. Geoffrey and Elizabeth Thayer Verney Fellowship
Georgen Gilliam, Curator of Library and Archives
Nantucket Historical Association
P.O. Box 1016
Nantucket, MA 02554-1016
Tel. 508.228.1655
georgen@nha.org
http://www.nha.org/verney%20fellowship.htm
Deadline: December 1

Up to three weeks housing in the historical Thomas Macy House, a $200 weekly stipend, and a one-year membership in the NHA is awarded to an academic, graduate student, or independent scholar conducting research in the NHA collections. "Topics of research for recent scholars have included health aboard whaleships, women at sea, scrimshaw, samplers, local artists, Nantucket's architectural heritage, Quakerism, the African-American and Cape Verdean community, the Quaise Asylum, and abolitionism." Visiting Research Scholars are expected to produce an article suitable for publication in the NHA's quarterly journal, *Historic Nantucket*. Applicants should send a description of the proposed project, a preliminary bibliography, a *curriculum vitae*, and the names of three references, and should include anticipated time and duration of stay.

79
Rose Voci Fellowship for Women
Writers' Center of Indiana
P.O. Box 30407
Indianapolis, IN 46230-0407
Tel. 317.255.0710
http://www.indianawriters.org
Deadline: November 15

This fellowship is open to any woman living in Indiana, "who has a sincere desire to better herself as a working writer." The first place winner wins a $1,000 award; two second place winners win $250 or weekend retreats at the Mary Anderson Center for the Arts at Mt. St. Francis, Indiana. Applicants must write a letter, maximum two pages in length, "describing how the $1,000 fellowship award will better their writing lives." Entries should be sent via postal mail to the above address.

80
Wesleyan Writers' Conference Teaching Fellowships
Anne Greene, Conference Director
Wesleyan Writers Conference,
Middletown, CT 06459
Tel. 860.685.3604
agreene@wesleyan.edu
http://www.wesleyan.edu/writers
Deadline: April 11 (received)

Teaching fellowships for this annual conference, held in June at Wesleyan University, are awarded in fiction, non-fiction and poetry to applicants who are generally expected to have completed a book-length manuscript. Fellows "work informally with Conference participants, organizing readings and offering editorial advice." Fellowships include conference tuition, room and board and offer a $500 honorarium per Fellow. To apply, submit the conference registration form along with a "representative sample" of your work and a letter of application. Note: Some scholarships are also available for this conference, with information also provided on the website.

81
Weymouth Center for the Arts and Humanities
Rosemary Holland, Administrator
Writers in Residence Program
555 East Connecticut Avenue
PO Box 939
Southern Pines, NC 28388
Tel. 910.692.6261
weymouthcenter@pinehurst.net

http://www.weymouthcenter.org
Rolling application

The Weymouth Center offers up to two weeks' housing for published writers ("North Carolina natives or current residents or those with significant ties to the state"). Contact Ms. Holland for additional information.

CHAPTER NINE
Student Opportunities
(Undergraduate and Graduate)

Having recently completed a graduate program in creative writing, and having taught a number of talented writers in many disciplines for the past several years, I know how valuable these opportunities specifically targeted for student writers can be. The financial rewards are perhaps obvious, but the boost from publication, prestige—and confidence—that can result from a contest win at a formative stage in a student writer's career also deserves some attention.

82
Atlantic Monthly Student Writing Contest
77 N. Washington Street
Boston, MA 02114
http://www.theatlantic.com/about/contest.htm
Deadline: December 1 (postmarked)

For undergraduate or graduate students currently enrolled in an accredited degree-granting U.S. institution. Categories include poetry, fiction, and personal/journalistic essays; entrants may submit no more than one submission per category. Prizes include cash awards for the top three entrants in each category ($1,000/$500/$250) and one-year subscriptions to the magazine for the seven runners-up in each group. Submissions, which should be unpublished work (publication in student periodicals is acceptable) should be accompanied by a cover sheet that includes the work's title, category, word count, author's name, address, phone number, e-mail address (if available), and academic institution. Only the title of the work should appear on the manuscript itself. Entrants should also include a stamped, self-addressed postcard for acknowledgment of receipt.

83
Jane Austen Society of North America Essay Contest

Joan Klingel Ray
Professor and President's Teaching Scholar
Chair, Department of English
University of Colorado at Colorado Springs
PO Box 7150
1420 Austin Bluffs Parkway
Colorado Springs, CO 80933-7150
JaneBRS@starband.net
http://www.jasnaa.org/essay_contest.html
Deadline: May 1

Submissions welcome from high school students, full and part-time undergraduate students, and full and part-time graduate students (essays will be judged in these categories). Prize packages combine cash award, publication, and/or admission and lodging at the Society's Annual Meeting. Full rules and suggestions to help with the essay writing process are available on the website.

84
Bucknell Seminar for Younger Poets
Stadler Center for Poetry
Bucknell Hall
Bucknell University
Lewisburg, PA 17837
Tel. 570.577.1853
stadlercenter@bucknell.edu
http://www.bucknell.edu/StadlerCenter/
Deadline: February 25 (postmarked)

"Held for four weeks during June on the campus of Bucknell University, the Seminar provides an extended opportunity for undergraduate poets to write and be guided by established poets and writers." Applicants (who must be students completing their sophomore, junior, or senior year in a U.S. college/university in May 2004) compete for 10-12 fellowships, which include tuition, housing, and meals. "A limited number of travel scholarships are available and are awarded on the basis of need." Application packets must include a letter discussing the applicant's "commitment to poetry" and goals for the seminar; if a need-based travel scholarship is requested that should be addressed in the letter as well. Two letters of recommendation, an official transcript, and a sample of poems (maximum 12 typed pages) should also be included.

85
Sylvia K. Burack Scholarship
The Writer
21027 Crossroads Circle
P.O. Box 1612

Waukesha, WI 53187-1612
http://www.writermag.com
Deadline: March 1 (postmarked)

For a full-time student enrolled in a U.S. or Canadian university who writes the best essay on the topic: "The importance of writing in the 21st century." In addition to the scholarship, the winning student will have his/her essay published in *The Writer* and he or she will receive a subscription to *The Writer* and a copy of *The Writer's Handbook*. Essays of 600-800 words should be submitted via postal mail to the address above. The manuscript should have the essay title—but not the writer's name—at the top of each page. Include a cover page with the essay title, word count, author's name, address, phone number, and e-mail address. Pages must be numbered and the essay must be paper-clipped.

86
Dante Prize

Dante Society of America
P.O. Box 0711
Framingham, MA 01701-0711
dsa@dantesociety.org
http://www.dantesociety.org/prizes.html
Deadline: June 30

The Dante Society offers a $250 award for best essay on a subject related to the life and works of Dante written by an undergraduate in an American or Canadian college or university. Also eligible are recent graduates (within the past year) who are not enrolled as graduate students. (Another prize, for $500, the Grandgent Award, is offered for a graduate essay.) Winning essays are published in the Dante Society's *Newsletter* and in *Dante Studies*. Essays must be submitted by e-mail attachment to the Dante Society. See web guidelines for specific instructions.

87
Emily Dickinson International Society Graduate Student Fellowship
c/o Professor Mary Loeffelholz
Department of English
406 Holmes Hall
Northeastern University
Boston, MA 02115
m.loeffelholz@neu.edu
http://www.cwru.edu/affil/edis/edisindex.html
Deadline: March 30 (received)

This $500 fellowship, whose first recipient will receive the award in 2004, supports graduate student scholarship on Emily Dickinson. The fellowship is intended "to fund travel to collections or conferences, to support book purchases, or for other research expenses necessary to the project." Applications, which may be submitted by mail or electronically to Professor Loeffelholz at the addresses above, must include a curriculum vitae, a project description, the names and contact information of two references, and a dissertation prospectus "or other relevant writing sample" no longer than 25 pages. Award will be announced by May 15. Note: preference for this fellowship award will be given to those enrolled in doctoral programs and writing dissertations "or other major projects directed toward publications."

88
Freedom Forum-NCAA Sports Journalism Scholarship

Sports Journalism Scholarship Committee
Attn: Suzy Hays
NCAA
P.O. Box 6222
Indianapolis, IN 46206-6222
Tel. 317.917.6816
http://www.ncaa.org
Deadline: December (check for 2004 deadline; in 2003 it was December 12, postmarked)

Awards eight $3,000 scholarships to college juniors "to assist them in their senior year of study. The program is specifically designed to foster freedoms of speech and press while promoting quality sports journalism education at the collegiate level." See website for application form and guidelines.

89
Bobette Bibo Gugliotta Memorial Scholarship for Creative Writing

Peninsula Community Foundation
Wendy Edwards, Scholarships Coordinator
1700 South El Camino Real, Suite 300
San Mateo, CA 94402-3049
Tel. 650.358.9369
wedwards@pcf.org
http://www.pcf.org/community_grants/scholarships.html#bbgmscw
Deadline: March (in 2003, March 5, received)

Intended to benefit students majoring in creative writing "who have demonstrated creative writing ability," this program awards one $1000 prize for a graduating high school senior and one $2000 prize for an undergraduate or graduate student. "Applicants must be United States citizens and must attend, or have graduated from, high schools located in San Mateo County or northern Santa Clara County.") Application information packet available for downloading on the website. (Among her other achievements, Mrs. Gugliotta wrote a story—at the age of 11—about a mouse that later became Mickey....)

90
Health Communications Internship Program
National Cancer Institute
Attn. Internship Director
Building 31, Room 10A28
31 Center Drive, MSC 2580
Bethesda, MD 20892-2580
Tel. 301.496.4394
NCIinterndirector@mail.nih.gov
http://intership.cancer.gov
Deadlines: March 15 (July-December session); September 15 (January-June session; postmarked)

For students (U.S. citizens) with some science background, enrolled in programs leading to the master's or doctoral degree, interested in the areas of health communications and science writing. The National Cancer Institute offers stipends—calculated on relevant work experience and undergraduate GPA, health insurance, and other benefits during the internship, which lasts a minimum of six months and may be renewed up to 1 year. NCI offices that have accepted communication interns include the Office of Communications, Office of Education and Special Initiatives, Office of Liaison Activities, Office of Cancer Complementary and Alternative Medicine, Division of Epidemiology and Genetics, Division of Cancer Prevention, Division of Cancer Control and Population Sciences. See website for detailed guidelines.

91
Hurston/Wright Award for College Writers
6525 Belcrest Road
Suite 531
Hyattsville, MD 20782
Tel. 301.683.2134
info@hurston-wright.org
http://hurston-wright.org/hw_award.html
Deadline: December 31 (postmarked)

Established by novelist Marita Golden, the Zora Neale Hurston/Richard Wright Award recognizes "excellence in fiction writing by students of African descent enrolled full time as undergraduate or graduate students in any college or university in the United States." Short stories and novel excerpts are eligible (entrants should indicate whether the submission is a short story or a novel excerpt). One entry per writer is permitted. Entries should not exceed 25 pages. Writer's name should not appear on the manuscript, but a cover page should include writer's name, address, phone number, and school name. First place award of $1,000 and two finalist awards of $500 presented at a ceremony in Washington, DC.

92
Kerlan Essay Award
113 Elmer L. Andersen Library
University of Minnesota
222 21st Avenue South
Minneapolis, MN 55455
Tel. 612.624.4576
http://special.lib.umn.edu/clrc/awards.html#2
Deadline: June 1 (postmarked)

Awarded for an outstanding paper written during the preceding school year by a college or university student. The paper must have used the resources of the Children's Literature Research Collections at the University of Minnesota. The prize includes $300 and a citation. Telephone the library for specific submission instructions.

93
Ruth Lilly Poetry Fellowships
The Poetry Foundation
1030 North Clark Street
Suite 420
Chicago, IL 60610
Tel. 312.787.7070
http://www.poetrymagazine.org/ruth_lilly_fellowships.html
Deadline: April 15 (postmarked)

Two fellowships, each for $15,000, are awarded annually "for use in further studies of poetry." This national competition is open to undergraduates and graduate students in creative writing or English. "Students must be American citizens under thirty years old and must not have published a collection of poetry or had one accepted for further publication." Nominations are required; there is an alternative nomination process for poets who meet the eligibility criteria but have not attended graduate school. There is also an official application form. See website for details.

94
National Association of Hispanic Journalists
Scholarship Committee
Kevin Olivas, NAHJ Educational Programs Manager
1000 National Press Building
529 14th Street, NW
Washington, DC 20045-2001
Tel. 202.662.7145
kolivas@nahj.org
http://www.nahj.org/student.html
Deadline: January 30 (postmarked)

The NAHJ offers several scholarship opportunities for current high school seniors, college undergraduates, and first-year graduate students, including the Rubén Salazar Scholarship, the Newhouse Scholarship Program for current college sophomores, and the NAHJ Newsroom Bound Program. Some scholarships offer multi-year funding (the Newhouse Scholarship offers $5,000 each year for two years for college students pursuing careers in English-language newspaper journalism). Factors NAHJ considers in candidates' applications include commitment to the field of journalism, academic achievement, financial need, and awareness of the community.

95
National Federation of State Poetry Societies College/University Level Poetry Competition Awards

Sybella Beyer-Snyder, Chairman
3444 South Dover Terrace
Inverness, FL 34452-7116
Tel. 1.352.344.3456
sybella@digitalusa.net
http://www.nfsps.com/scholarship.htm
Submissions (including notarized entry form): January 1-February 1 (received)

For freshmen, sophomores, juniors and seniors at accredited colleges and universities. Two students will win $500 awards and stipend to travel to the June NFSPS convention, where they will be invited to read from their work. The award manuscripts are published, with each recipient receiving 75 copies of the published work. Submission package must include notarized application form, available on the website.

96
Elie Wiesel Prize in Ethics Essay Contest

Elie Wiesel Foundation for Humanity
529 Fifth Avenue Suite 1802
New York, NY 10017
Tel. 212.490.7777
epinfo@eliewieselfoundation.org
http://www.eliewieselfoundation.org/EthicsPrize/EPContest.htm
Deadline: December (in 2003: Dec. 5, postmarked)

Open to full-time undergraduate juniors and seniors at accredited four-year colleges and universities. Essay topics suggested on website, though "Students may write about anything as long as it pertains to ethics." First prize ($5,000); Second Prize ($2,500); Third Prize ($1,500); two Honorable Mentions of $500 each. Comprehensive submission guidelines, including entry form, available on the website.

CHAPTER TEN
Emergency Funding

Illness. Natural disasters. Financial struggles. Legal troubles. Lots of reasons can compel writers to seek emergency funding. Here are a few resources that offer assistance in those difficult situations.

97
American Poets Fund
Academy of American Poets
588 Broadway, Suite 604
New York, NY 10012-3210
Tel. 212.274.0343
http://www.poets.org/awards/apfund.cfm

Offers limited, "confidential assistance to poets in the event of illness of other emergency." Applicants cannot apply directly; nominations (made in writing to the Executive Director) must come from Academy Chancellors, Fellows, and award-winners.

98
Louisiana Division of the Arts Director's Grant-in-Aid Program
P.O. Box 44247
Baton Rouge, LA 70804-4247
Tel. 225.342.8180
arts@crt.state.la.us

http://www.crt.state.la.us/arts/state_art_grant/dirgiaid.htm

Provides "enhanced assistance to meet critical and unforeseen needs of professional Louisiana artists and non-profit 501(c)(3) arts organizations." Funds may be used to cover replacement costs for supplies/materials "lost or damaged in natural disasters." See website for guidelines on eligibility and application procedures. Note: This program also may fund travel/participation costs for "special career opportunities."

99
PEN Writers' Fund
Victoria Kupchinestsky, Coordinator
568 Broadway 4th Floor
New York, NY 10012
Tel. 212.334.1660, ext. 116
victoria@pen.org
http://www.pen.org/writfund.html

For professional ("published or produced") writers "with serious financial difficulties." May provide grants or loans of up to $1,000. This is not a fund for research, project-completion, or for the funding of publications or organizations. "The maximum amount is given only under especially dire circumstances and when monies are available." Note: The PEN Writers' Fund, which meets approximately bimonthly to review applications, also administers the PEN Fund for Writers and Editors with HIV/AIDS. Contact Victoria Kupchinetsky for information on both funds.

100
The Working Fund
c/o Samuel S. Fleisher Art Memorial
709-721 Catharine Street
Philadelphia, PA 19147
Tel. 215.922.3456, x22
workfund@critpath.org
http://www.critpath.org/workfund/wfgrant.htm

Awards cash grants to artists in any discipline, who live in Bucks, Chester, Delaware, Montgomery, Philadelphia, or Camden County and "whose work has been interrupted or seriously impaired by HIV/AIDS." Applicants should submit a short (maximum 2-page) letter proposal and include a budget, names and telephone numbers of two references familiar with the applicant's work who can also verify financial need, statement from a health care provider confirming HIV/AIDS diagnosis, current professional resume (if applicable) and work samples (as supplements).

101
Writers Emergency Assistance Fund
American Society of Journalists and Authors Charitable Trust
1501 Broadway, Suite 302
New York, NY 10036
Tel. 212.997.0947
http://www.asja.org//weaf.php

Formerly the Llewellyn Miller Fund, this source "exists to help established freelance non-fiction writers across the country who, because of advancing age, illness, disability, or extraordinary professional crisis are unable to work." Grant applicants "must be sixty years of age or older, or be so disabled that their normal writing capacity has been severely diminished, or—regardless of age or disability— be caught up in an extraordinary professional crisis (such as a lawsuit) where a grant would help." Applications may be obtained from the ASJA office, and application packets must include samples of the applicant's published work; financial documentation; and professional and medical references.

CHAPTER ELEVEN
Additional Sources/References

The following print and online sources should assist you in finding even more opportunities—and additional practical advice on how best to pursue them. Make it a habit of finding and checking—frequently—your own sources for opportunities.

In Print:

Fennelly, Beth Ann. "The Winnowing of Wildness: On First Book Contests and Style." *The Writer's Chronicle* October-November 2003: 53-54.

PEN American Center. *Grants and Awards Available to American Writers*. 2002-03 edition. Ed. John Morrone. New York: PEN American Center.

Perry, Katherine. "Fast Track: Literary Contests and Book Publication." *The Writer* October 2003: 27-29.

Poets&Writers. November/December 2003. Contains several articles "On Contests," offering insights from a sponsor, a judge, and a contest coordinator.

On the Web:

General Contest Guidance and Resources

(These resources include both "fee-free" opportunities and those that may require application/processing/ reading fees.)

Allison Joseph's Creative Writers' Opportunities List
http://www.topica.com/lists/crwropps
Frequent updates available by (free) subscription; archives available to the public.

Poetry Magazine's Contest Page
http://poetrymagazine.com/contests.htm
Offers a compact, useful list.

Resources for Artists
http://www.pewarts.org/resources.html
Excellent annotated list on the Pew Fellowships site. Similar lists offered on the site for media arts and other disciplines.

"Warnings and Cautions for Writers/Writing Contests and Vanity Anthologies." Updated 29 October 2003. http://www.sfwa.org/beware/contests.html
Cited 14 November 2003.
From Writer Beware. Advice on approaching and assessing contests, and links to several very practical how-to articles to help writers evaluate, enter and win competitions,

WinningWriters.com
http://www.winningwriters.com
Contests—and much more. Jendi Reiter and Adam Cohen maintain this comprehensive site for poets (especially) and other writers. Resources include their online guide to poetry contests (*Poetry Contest Insider*), manuscript tips for poets, recommendations on supplies and tools for writers, and more.

Grants and Granstmanship

Grants and Fellowships for the Arts
http://www.library.arizona.edu/users/juarezm/artfun.htm l
Maintained at the University of Arizona; includes sections on websites and searchable databases, grants to individuals, grant writing guides, and other practical information.

Grants for Individuals: Arts
http://www.lib.msu.edu/harris23/grants/3arts.htm
Maintained at Michigan State University: comprehensive listings of websites, databases, books, and announcements.

GRAPES
UCLA Graduate and Postdoctoral Extramural Support (GRAPES) Database
http://www.gdnet.ucla.edu/grpinst.htm
This UCLA-maintained database contains information on approximately 400 programs, searchable by discipline and academic level.

National Assembly of State Arts Agencies
http://www.nasaa-arts.org/aoa/saaweb.shtml
Includes links to state arts agencies/councils and their resources, including funding opportunities. It's worth noting that many state art agencies and councils maintain regular newsletters and lists of resources available open to artists nationwide.

Potter, Megan. "Grants, Fellowships and Residencies: What Do They Mean to You?"
http://www.writersweekly.com/this_weeks_article/00061 0_09052001.html
Cited 14 November 2003.
From WritersWeekly.com—the title says it all.

"Proposal Writing Short Course."
http://fdncenter.org/learn/shortcourse/prop1.html
Cited 14 November 2003.
Here you'll find informative instructions from The Foundation Center.

Other Useful Information

Alliance of Artists Communities
http://www.artistcommunities.org/
Information on colonies, residencies, and related organizations.

Free Scholarship Search Databases
http://scholarships.kachinatech.com/scholar5.html
Includes scholarships, fellowships, and postdoctoral awards.

FundsforWriters.com
http://www.fundsforwriters.com
C. Hope Clark's resource-laden site, including information on subscription to her various opportunity-filled newsletters (many for free).

NYFA Interactive
http://www.nyfa.org
One of the most extensive databases available allowing searches for grants, fellowships, residencies, and other career-related opportunities, courtesy of the New York Foundation for the Arts website and sponsors .

WriteSuccess.com
http://www.writesuccess.com
Maintained by Mary Anne Hahn, this well-organized site offers, among other items, links to sites featuring contests, markets, jobs, and other resources for writers.

APPENDIX A
Your Calendar

*Use this space to make a note of deadlines, month-by-month, for the contests, competitions and opportunities that interest you most. Include page numbers from **Free Expression**, where applicable. Don't forget to check back here frequently to keep yourself on schedule!*

January

Feb

March

April

May

June

July

August

September

October

November

December

APPENDIX B
Favorite Resources

Use this space to list additional sources that are useful to you. Consider books on writing, favorite writing exercises, inspirational quotations, beloved poems, writing magazines/ezines, websites, databases, or anything else that helps you think about your writing life in the broadest, most potential-filled terms possible.

APPENDIX C
Additional Possibilities

Use this page to note any additional writing contests, competitions, or other opportunities that you may have discovered/plan to pursue. (Why stop at 101???)

ABOUT THE AUTHOR

ERIKA DREIFUS earned undergraduate and graduate degrees from Harvard University, where she taught history and literature 1996-2002 and where she has also taught in the Extension School Writing Program. In 2003 she earned the Master of Fine Arts degree in Creative Writing from Queens University of Charlotte, NC. She contributes frequently to print and online publications on the craft and business of writing.

A 2003 Writer-in-Residence at the Kimmel Harding Nelson Center for the Arts and 2002 Vermont Studio Center Resident in Fiction, she has won grants and fellowships from the Krupp Foundation, the Minda de Gunzburg Center for European Studies, and the Charles Warren Center for Studies in American History. In 2003 her short story, "Homecomings," was named first place winner in the David Dornstein Memorial Creative Writing Contest for Young Adult Writers.

Printed in the United States
1519400001B/388-411